America Becomes
a World Power

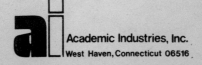

Academic Industries, Inc.
West Haven, Connecticut 06516

ISBN 0-88301-868-3

Published by
Academic Industries,Inc.
The Academic Building
Saw Mill Road
West Haven, Connecticut 06516

Printed in the United States of America

contents

Both France and Spain had hoped to build up their colonies in America. But in the Louisiana Purchase Napoleon sold his French lands to the United States. The Spanish colonies in South America then won their freedom. At that time these new nations were still young and weak. Therefore, in 1823, President Monroe announced the Monroe Doctrine. This warned that there could be no new colonies in either North or South America.

In 1863, Napoleon III, Emperor of France, sent a French army into Mexico.

The United States was fighting the Civil War. Secretary of State Seward talked with President Lincoln.

After helping the South in every way he could, Napoleon has now taken over Mexico!

This is clearly against the Monroe Doctrine. He counts on it that we are too busy with the South to fight France.

Which is true. Try to get word to the Mexicans that we have not forgotten them. After we have won the war, we will take action.

Napoleon made an Austrian nobleman, Maximilian, the Emperor of Mexico. With his wife Carlota he went there.

I have been told that the Mexican people wish me to rule them!

You will be a fine emperor!

In Mexico, Maximilian and Carlota were crowned.

7

When the Civil War ended, the United States rushed 50,000 soldiers to the Mexican border. They would see that the Monroe Doctrine was kept.

In France, Louis Napoleon was angry.

Those Americans! Bring the French soldiers home from Mexico!

The Mexicans had not really wanted an emperor.

The French soldiers are returning home! We will have our own government again!

Viva Juarez!

I do not know what will happen here. You must sail for Europe!

Louis Napoleon is leaving you here with no one to help you!

In the same year, 1867, Secretary Seward had a visitor.

The Russian ambassador, Edward de Stoeckl, to see you, sir.

Well, show him in!

After the greetings, Stoeckl made an offer.

Our land in Alaska is too far from Russia. The cost of protecting and using it is too great. We would like to sell it to the United States.

If we can agree on a price, I will take the matter to Congress.

The price, $7,200,000, was less than two cents an acre for half a million square miles. Congress agreed. But some Americans did not.

What do you think of "Seward's Folly"?

The icebox, you mean? Alaska? Nothing but a frozen waste-land.

The Indian slaves in Alaska were set free when it became American land. They carved a wooden statue.

It is Abraham Lincoln, the Great Emancipator!

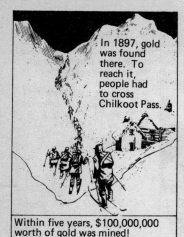

In 1897, gold was found there. To reach it, people had to cross Chilkoot Pass.

Within five years, $100,000,000 worth of gold was mined!

Navy bases were soon set up. Today in the air age, some important air bases are there.

Soon a pipeline will cross Alaska, bringing much-needed oil to continental United States.

Oil and other minerals have been found in Alaska. Now "Seward's Folly" is a rich country, and the forty-ninth state of the Union.

★★★★

Other events also helped America to become a world power. They took place thousands of miles away, in the middle of the Pacific Ocean, on the Hawaiian Islands.

Both the climate and the people of the Hawaiian Islands were friendly. American ships found these harbors good places to stop for supplies.

About 1820, American missionaries came to the Islands to start churches and schools.

Most Hawaiians became Christians.

These are the children of the wealthy. Someday we hope to have schools for all Hawaiian children.

It is not right! This school teaches our children the ways of the Haoles and the worship of their God!

The God of the Missionaries is the true God! Our old gods lost their powers long ago!

More and more people came to Hawaii. In 1842 there was frightening news.

A British ship is in the harbor. Its guns are aimed at Honolulu. They are trying to take over the Kingdom of Hawaii.

My mother the queen will never give in!

But there was no defense against the British guns. The Hawaiian flag was taken down. The British flag was raised.

Dr. Judd, an American missionary, was chief adviser to the Hawaiian queen.

I have written about this to the English. I have sent it by secret messenger to Queen Victoria.

For five months the British ruled Hawaii. Then another British ship sailed into the harbor.

In the schoolroom, Mrs. Cooke talked to her class again.

There is wonderful news! Queen Victoria has ordered that Hawaii be given back to the Hawaiians. The queen will rule again!

After this, American missionaries continued to help the Hawaiian queen.

Hawaii must have a constitution and elections. Land should be divided among all the people.

But my people do not know about these things!

POCKET HISTORY

This proved to be true. Owning land for the first time, the Hawaiians sold it for a few dollars. Soon there were large plantations of sugar cane. More Americans arrived, and many Hawaiians married them. The islands soon wanted closer ties to the United States. They also wanted the same form of government. Plans were made to do this.

In 1893, American marines came ashore from the *U.S.S. Boston.*

After a peaceful revolution Queen Liliuokalani gave up her throne.

Once again the Hawaiian flag was lowered. This time the flag of the United States went up.

We have done what we believe to be for the best. You must accept it, or there will be fighting.

The new government asked to be added to the United States. In 1898, this was done. Finally, in 1959, Hawaii became the fiftieth state of the Union.

In 1851 the Secretary of State, Daniel Webster, talked to Commodore Matthew Perry of the U. S. Navy.

For more than 200 years, Japan has been closed to the rest of the world. I want you to try to open the door to Americans!

Yes, sir!

You will try to get help for sailors shipwrecked in Japan. You will try to open their ports to ships which need supplies. And we would like to have them open trade with us.

You will lead the largest American fleet ever sent to the Far East. But your job is peaceful! Fighting is to be used only to defend yourselves.

I understand, sir!

The "largest fleet" was two steamships and two sailing boats. They looked small in the Great China Sea.

15

As they neared Tokyo Bay, the sailors talked.

We're heading for a trap! There are thirty million Japanese, and we've only got four ships.

I hear they lock shipwrecked sailors up in cages—like animals!

The American ships anchored in the bay. A group of rowboats from the shore came out to them.

A blast from an American steam whistle frightened one Japanese crew.

WHEEEEEEEEE

They are living in the Middle Ages! For 200 years they have let no one into Japan. They have allowed no Japanese to leave.

They have a lot of catching up to do!

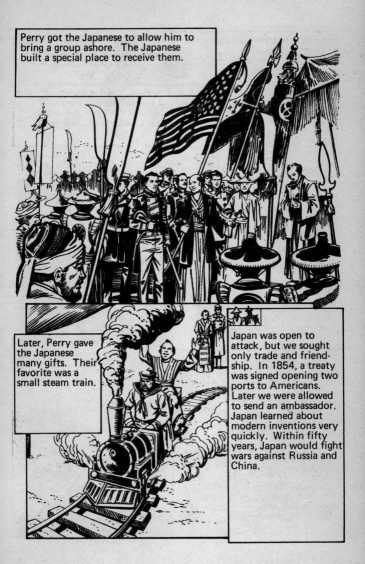

Perry got the Japanese to allow him to bring a group ashore. The Japanese built a special place to receive them.

Later, Perry gave the Japanese many gifts. Their favorite was a small steam train.

Japan was open to attack, but we sought only trade and friendship. In 1854, a treaty was signed opening two ports to Americans. Later we were allowed to send an ambassador. Japan learned about modern inventions very quickly. Within fifty years, Japan would fight wars against Russia and China.

Cuba, an island off the Florida coast, had belonged to Spain since 1492. Its people had become slaves and suffered a great deal. In the 1890s, many Americans wanted to fight Spain to free Cuba.

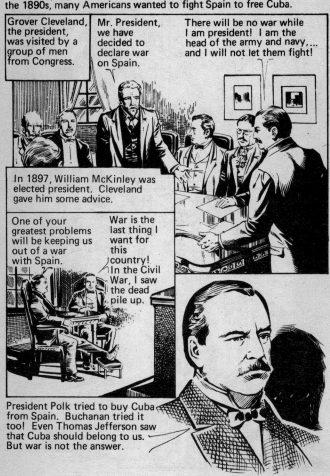

Grover Cleveland, the president, was visited by a group of men from Congress.

Mr. President, we have decided to declare war on Spain.

There will be no war while I am president! I am the head of the army and navy, ... and I will not let them fight!

In 1897, William McKinley was elected president. Cleveland gave him some advice.

One of your greatest problems will be keeping us out of a war with Spain.

War is the last thing I want for this country! In the Civil War, I saw the dead pile up.

President Polk tried to buy Cuba from Spain. Buchanan tried it too! Even Thomas Jefferson saw that Cuba should belong to us. But war is not the answer.

Talking things over, that is the way. But there is so much sympathy for Cuba...

And so many un-true stories in the press!

Exactly! You may be forced into war.

God help me to stay out of it!

John D. Long was made Secretary of the navy, with Theodore Roosevelt to help him.

I like young Roosevelt, John. But he tends to stir things up too much! I depend on you to keep him quiet.

I'll do my best.

Roosevelt was sent to look over a torpedo boat, under repair after an accident.

Great! Bully!

Roosevelt sent in his report.

Torpedo boats must run great risks. It is more important that officers handle them with daring than that they should be kept unscratched!

Sir, this hardly sounds like the usual navy report!

Would you say this shows a new spirit in the navy?

It shows my feeling that we must have a *better* navy!

Roosevelt learned that not enough money was set aside to train navy men in target practice. He ordered that nearly a million dollars be spent for this.

Good! They're improving! Keep up the practice!

Theodore, we must not waste so much money shooting into the sea.

Sir, we have a new type of gun. The men must learn how to use it. The only shots that count are the ones that hit!

In a talk at the Naval War College in Newport, he asked for a stronger navy.

Being ready for war is the best way to keep the peace. It is too late to prepare for war when the time of peace has passed!

For years Cuban guerrillas had been fighting the Spaniards. Some were led by General Garcia.

In return, the Spaniards brought in General Weyler to rule.

All over the island, we will burn the sugar mills.

So. They burn the mills. We will burn the cane fields!

21

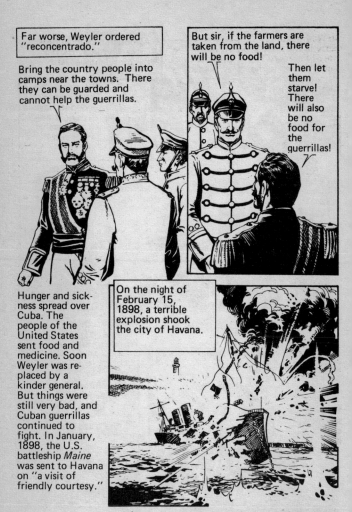

Far worse, Weyler ordered "reconcentrado."

Bring the country people into camps near the towns. There they can be guarded and cannot help the guerrillas.

But sir, if the farmers are taken from the land, there will be no food!

Then let them starve! There will also be no food for the guerrillas!

Hunger and sickness spread over Cuba. The people of the United States sent food and medicine. Soon Weyler was replaced by a kinder general. But things were still very bad, and Cuban guerrillas continued to fight. In January, 1898, the U.S. battleship *Maine* was sent to Havana on "a visit of friendly courtesy."

On the night of February 15, 1898, a terrible explosion shook the city of Havana.

The battleship *Maine* had blown up in Havana harbor.

In Washington, early in the morning of February 16, lights burned in the navy department. Messengers hurried through the quiet city.

At dawn, the president was awakened.

Although he had a house guest, Myron T. Herrick, the president was late for breakfast.

To Secretary Long's house.

Sir, an important message from Secretary Long.

What is it?

You're late, sir! And you look very stern today.

There's bad news. The *Maine* exploded in Havana harbor. She sank with more than 250 of her men.

My God, sir! What caused it?

No one knows. But we will study it right away. The country must not fight back until the truth is known!

23

But the people wanted to fight!

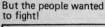

Extra! *Maine* blown up! Hundreds of sailors killed!

Isn't it terrible? Does it mean war?

Of course it means war! Would we let Spain get away with this?

We could send 600 Sioux Indians to scalp the Spanish!

How about a crowd of Indian fighters, under Colonel Buffalo Bill Cody?

Remember the *Maine*! That's our motto.

The U. S. Pacific ships were at anchor in Hong Kong harbor. One day when Secretary Long was away, Roosevelt sent a message to the commander.

To Dewey, Hong Kong, China. Keep full of coal. If war begins, see that the Spanish ships do not leave the coast of Asia. We will fight in the Philippine Islands!

Commodore Dewey went to work.

Order more gunpowder. Get coal from everywhere...try Wales, too. And I want all the charts, maps, everything we have on the Philippines.

All white paint must be covered with gray.

On April 24, 1898, Dewey received the message he had waited for.

War has begun between the United States and Spain! We will go at once to the Philippines to fight the Spanish!

Dewey had four fighting ships, one gunboat, and three supply ships. European navy officers in Hong Kong had been making bets to Dewey's officers. They believed the Americans would be defeated by the Spanish. But the little group sailed with great hope. Three nights later they lay off Manila Bay.

I'll take a chance on underwater mines. But we haven't the armor to fight against their coast-defense guns.

We must enter the harbor in darkness. No lights except a small guiding light on each ship.

In the blackout, Dewey on the *Olympia* led the way. Suddenly soot in the smokestack of the *McCulloch* caught fire! Soon from Corregidor a signal rocket rose into the sky.

It has taken them a long time to wake up!

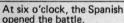

At six o'clock, the Spanish opened the battle.

Sixteen merchant ships at anchor, sir, and eleven enemy warships.

And, of course, the coast defense guns behind them.

With the ship's captain, Charles Gridley, beside him, Dewey watched as his ships drew closer.

Now! You may fire when you are ready, Gridley.

Although the Spanish had more ships, the Americans had more guns and were better shooters.

The Spanish fought bravely. But at 12:30 P.M., their ships sunk or in flames, they surrendered. There were 167 Spanish dead, 250 wounded. Dewey only had seven men wounded. The Americans were in control of Manila Bay.

While Dewey had prepared for war in Hong Kong, Washington prepared too. The president waited for a report on the *Maine*.

Mr. President. Congress has voted fifty million dollars for your use in the national defense!

I still hope for peace, but we must prepare for war.

The report arrived on March 24. McKinley talked with his cabinet.

The navy divers found signs of outside damage. The shot must have set off the ship's own magazines.

Nothing to show who shot at the *Maine*?

Nothing at all. It could even have been a rebel, hoping to cause trouble for Spain.

It did indeed cause trouble for Spain. Senator Henry Cabot Lodge of Massachusetts gave a report.

I believe the *Maine* was blown up by a government mine. I'm sure the Spanish had a high-ranking officer in charge.

Both the people and Congress agreed with Lodge.

Due in part to Roosevelt, the navy was ready for action. Dewey won the first victory of the war. Secretary of War Alger called for more soldiers.

I am raising three cavalry units. I will make you an officer of the First U. S. Volunteer Cavalry!

No, sir. I've had too little training. Make Leonard Wood the officer, and I'll serve under him.

Very well, if that's the way you want it. You'll be lieutenant colonel.

28

Leonard Wood, an army doctor, had both medical and military skill.

I'm off to San Antonio where we'll train.

I've ordered a uniform from New York, a horse from Texas, and a dozen pairs of eyeglasses! I'll join you as soon as I can!

What sort of men have you lined up?

Harvard men: football players and tennis players. From the West, Indians and Indian fighters, cowboys, sheriffs. They're a good lot, sir!

The people of San Antonio were interested in the odd group of men, especially the cowboys.

By the time Roosevelt arrived, a large sign was hanging near the station.

Have you seen the latest group of "Teddy's Terrors"?

I've seen 'em and heard 'em! Those men are rough riders!

THIS WAY TO ROOSEVELT ROUGH RIDER CAMP

29

The army, under the command of General Shafter, was to ship out from Tampa, Florida.

But somehow, by June 22, 16,000 men were off the Cuban coast near Santiago.

Tell Alger that the troops are arriving without blankets, tents, uniforms, arms, ammunition, even without food! And we are very short of ships!

The Spaniards are reported to have 80,000 soldiers in Cuba. There are 36,000 on this eastern coast.

They'll attack us during the landing!

There was no way to land the animals. They were pushed overboard so they would swim to shore.

The men rode in lifeboats. At least two of them overturned.

But on the shore there were no Spaniards to be found. The American flag was raised as the soldiers cheered.

Shafter made his plans known.

We will move to Santiago and attack it from land. The navy will blockade the harbor, catching the Spaniards between the forces.

Between the Americans and Santiago, the Spaniards had dug trenches and placed barbed wire on the nearby hills. The Americans were stopped by enemy fire.

We must take that hill, boys. Forward! CHARGE!

With a cheer, the Rough Riders and soldiers of the black Ninth Cavalry followed Roosevelt up San Juan Hill.

They met a barbed-wire fence. Black soldiers rushed forward under fire from a Spanish fort.

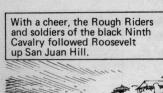

The battle was fierce. Again and again Roosevelt's men charged the fort. Finally the Americans won a victory.

The negro soldiers saved that fight.

Those men are all right!

America Becomes A World Power

The American soldiers closed in on Santiago. Part of the Spanish navy was blocked in the harbor by the American Atlantic ships. Trying to escape, the Spanish ships were destroyed by the Americans.

On July 16, the Spanish general Torel surrendered Santiago to General Shafter. The fight for Cuba was nearly over.

On July 25, General Miles and a group of Americans lay off the coast of Puerto Rico.

There it is. It's the only Spanish land left in the western hemisphere. We will take it and end the Spanish dream of colonies in the new world.

Miles landed on the south coast with 5,000 men. Within twenty days, the American flag was raised over the Puerto Rican capital, San Juan.

Commodore Dewey was on the other side of the world in the Philippines. News of his victory pleased and surprised people in the United States.

What's the parade for?

Celebrating Dewey's victory in the Philippines.

President McKinley and Secretary Long talked together.

That's great! But where are the Philippines?

Well... somewhere in the Pacific, I think.

Now we've got colonies like the other great countries.

I've sent Dewey our congratulations. I told him that he was to be made an admiral.

Good! And by the way... just where are the Philippines?

On August 12, less than four months after the war had begun, the United States and Spain agreed to end the fighting. But the peace treaty was put off by the problem of the Philippines.

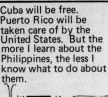

Cuba will be free. Puerto Rico will be taken care of by the United States. But the more I learn about the Philippines, the less I know what to do about them.

Senator Lodge has a large group who thinks we should keep them.

But the spirit that led this country into the war was not to gain more land. We wanted to help people who needed help.

Yet there are more than 5,000 different islands in the Philippines. There are many different races, tribes, religions. They are not prepared to govern themselves.

We can hardly return them to Spain!

No, no! And we can't turn them over to any European power or to Japan. There seems but one thing to do, and that is to keep them!

The Treaty of Paris was signed on December 10, 1898. By it, the United States became the owner of Puerto Rico, the Philippines, and the island of Guam. They paid Spain $20,000,000.

In Cuba the battles were over, but army men were still dying.

Sir, our men are becoming very sick! There are many new cases of fever and many deaths.

General Shafter called his officers together.

Malaria and dysentery are bad, but the real problem is yellow fever. No one knows the cause. It seems to spread in the night air.

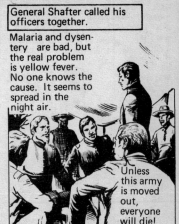

Unless this army is moved out, everyone will die!

The army was moved to the mainland except for the soldiers under General Wood. But the yellow fever stayed. In 1900 it spread widely among the Cubans.

We must end this fever once and for all! I am sending Dr. Walter Reed to study it.

Reed and his men arrived in Cuba.

As you know, sir, we have burned all clothes, bedding, everything that has touched people with the disease. But this has never stopped its spread.

Yes, Major...

We think it may be spread by the bite of a mosquito. I want to use some men in a test.

You may have whatever you need!

First, some men slept in the pajamas and beds of men who had died from yellow fever.

Sir, twenty nights have passed. We are still all healthy.

Thank God for that!

Reed asked for more men for another test. Private John Kissenger, a hospital aide, stepped forward.

You will be kept in a screened room with many mosquitoes. You know that I believe they carry the disease?

Yes, sir! But I will do it, sir!

Another man, John Moran, also helped with the test. In a few days, both men became very ill.

We must save them! I have never known two braver men!

Both men got better. Walter Reed had good news for General Wood and for the world.

Good news, sir. Yellow fever is spread by a mosquito. Control the mosquitoes and you control yellow fever!

Wonderful news, Major!

Send out an order to spread oil on all places where mosquitoes can breed.

At once, sir.

By 1901, there was not a single case of yellow fever in Havana. One of the greatest ills of the tropics had been conquered.

Other things were needed to make Cuba once more a fit place to live. The army fed the hungry, and cared for the sick. Roads, schools, public buildings were built or repaired. Wood also took steps to set up a government.

In November, 1900, the Cubans voted for delegates to a constitutional convention.

VOTO (AQUÍ)

Look, little one! Your father has fought against the Spanish for a free Cuba. Now he votes for one!

The United States asked for several favors. We wanted a navy at Guantanamo. We wanted the right to keep order in Cuba when it was needed.

General Wood told the Cuban leaders the feelings of the United States.

In May, 1902, the United States army left, and Cuba began to rule itself.

In 1934, by Cuba's demand, America's right to keep order was ended.

Secretary of War Alger left the cabinet. And Elihu Root got a phone call.

The president wishes you to become Secretary of War.

Thank him, but I cannot do it. I know nothing about war. I know nothing about the army.

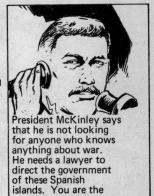

President McKinley says that he is not looking for anyone who knows anything about war. He needs a lawyer to direct the government of these Spanish islands. You are the lawyer he wants.

Elihu Root accepted the job. After doing his homework, he talked with the president.

The Puerto Rican people are poor. There are too many people, too little good land to feed them.

What steps should we take to help?

Take away our soldiers, set up a new government, and feed the people!

Shortly afterward, the island was hit by a hurricane.

The crops were ruined. President McKinley asked for money to help the people. Many Americans helped. War ships sailed to Puerto Rico with tons of supplies. Root gave them food from the army.

The United States was worried more about the Puerto Ricans' need for food than for a good government. But we had to help in that area, too.

They should be a "crown-colony."

Yes...a voting group elected by the people themselves, but with a governor named by myself as President.

We made some mistakes. But in 1917 the Puerto Ricans were made American citizens.

What does it mean— we are now United States citizens?

For one thing, we can go to the United States as people who live there—not as visitors!

Since then, Puerto Ricans have given many things to the American people.

Jose Ferrer is a great actor, director and producer. He was born in Santurce...

Two baseball players are Orlando Cepeda and Roberto Clemente.

And millions of Puerto Rican workers have come to live in the United States. They have taught us much about the Spanish way of life.

In 1948, there was an important election.

For the first time in 450 years, Puerto Ricans will elect their own governor!

The man elected was Luis Munoz Marin.

I am proud to be elected. I am happy that my fellow Puerto Ricans have voted to become a commonwealth.

The constitution of the Commonwealth of Puerto Rico went into effect on July 25, 1952.

In 1900, McKinley had talked about the Philippines with Elihu Root.

Two years ago Admiral Dewey said the Filipino rebels would not fight us. General Miles keeps saying they are conquered. But we still have a large army fighting in the Philippines!

I am sending General MacArthur to take charge.

General MacArthur spoke to the people.

Wherever the American flag goes, the idea of freedom goes.

But the Filipino rebel leader Aguinaldo and his guerrillas continued to fight.

Then Colonel Funston had a plan. With members of a tribe loyal to the Americans, he landed near Aguinaldo's hiding place.

For days they marched through the jungle toward Aguinaldo's hideout, acting as if Funston had been captured.

I have sent a message to Aguinaldo that we bring you as a captive!

Good!

Outside Aguinaldo's hiding place there was a fight, and Aguinaldo was captured before he knew what was happening.

The fighting ended. Aguinaldo became a citizen of the American Philippines. A government was set up. Under American rule the Filipinos improved their schools and government. On July 4, 1946, they became a free country.

POCKET HISTORY

In 1900 McKinley was elected president. Theodore Roosevelt became vice-president.

On September 6, 1901, the president greeted the crowd at the Pan-American Exposition at Buffalo. Suddenly a man with his hand covered drew near.

Pulling off the handkerchief, Leon Czolgosz fired two bullets.

Within eight days McKinley had died and Roosevelt was president. His first message to Congress was read on December 6.

To protect our interests in both the Atlantic and Pacific oceans, a canal joining the two must be built.

Ever since Columbus, people have looked for a water route to the Pacific. The Spanish talked of a canal. The French spent millions trying to build one.

If anybody can do it, it's Teddy Roosevelt!

The French canal company had valuable land in Panama. They would sell it to us if we built a canal there. But Panama was part of Colombia, and Colombia would not agree. French agents wanted them to separate from Colombia. In November, 1903, the people of Panama finally broke away from them. A new flag was raised over Panama City.

Two days later the United States recognized the Republic of Panama. Secretary Hay signed a treaty.

This treaty gives your country the right to build a canal.

Indeed, yes!

This proved to be the worst treaty the U. S. ever signed. But it did allow the building of the Panama Canal.

Colonel William Gorgas was the medical officer in charge. The great enemies were malaria and yellow fever.

We must have ditches to carry off the water, and oil for spraying.

He used as much as 50,000 gallons of oil a month. But Gorgas turned the canal zone into a health resort.

Colonel George Goethals was chief engineer of this huge job.

It will need the biggest locks in the world. The Gatun Dam will be the largest dam. Gatun lake will be the largest man-made body of water.

In 1906, Roosevelt himself came to see the canal.

It's bully!

On August 14, 1914, The S.S. *Ancon* made history. It was the first ship to pass through the Panama Canal. Everything worked perfectly.

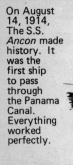

From the first, the canal was a success. But the people of Panama did not like the powers given to the United States by treaty. In 1964 they broke into the Canal Zone. A new treaty was worked out, but Panama is still not happy.

By 1980, if not sooner, the canal will be overcrowded. A new canal is being planned. It will be built in a new place at sea level (without locks) and will use atomic power.

In his first message to Congress, Roosevelt also talked about the big corporations — the Trusts.

They must be watched and controlled. Those who sell in other states should allow a full study of their business practices.

Later he gave orders to his Attorney General, Philander Knox.

Begin a lawsuit against the Northern Securities Company. They have not obeyed the Sherman Anti-trust law.

Yes, I agree. They have put many small companies out of business.

The railroads had joined together in the Northwest. The courts voted against the company. Soon lawsuits were brought against many such companies.

Roosevelt asked for a study of the meat and food companies. A government man reported.

The stockyards are terrible. And the companies that can our food are using colorings and other things that are not good for people.

A candy-maker who added pieces of bone to his coco-nut bars said, "It doesn't hurt the kids. They like it!"

That's too much!

And so Congress passed the Pure Food and Drug Act.

In 1902, the coal miners took their problems to John Mitchell, United Mine Workers' president.

Our year's pay is $560, and we don't even get that! They take money out for these company houses. And we have to buy at the company store.

And we all know mine work is dangerous.

We work ten to twelve hours a day.

I know very well, men. There's nothing to do but call a strike.

140,000 miners went on strike. The owners would not even talk to Mitchell. All summer, no coal was mined.

The whole country was worried. In October, Roosevelt called Mitchell and the mine owners to the White House for a talk.

Schools are closing for lack of coal. The price is so high that most people cannot buy it. I can't settle your argument, but you can do something about it.

Open the mines, go back to work, and let me help to settle your problem.

I accept your help, sir.

Never! Speaking for the owners, we will not accept.

Roosevelt was ready to order a group of soldiers to open the mines. But the mine owners finally agreed to give the men a ten percent increase in their pay. Soon they were back at work.

America Becomes A World Power

Since the country began, no one had thought much about its land. Roosevelt knew that it must be cared for.

Under the Reclamation Act of 1902, great dams were built in the West to water the dry land.

More than 3,000,000 acres of dry land were made useful.

A Forest Service was begun. Roosevelt's greatest supporter, Gifford Pinchot, was in charge.

Many people want the forests for their own profit.

We will save some of them for the country!

Roosevelt changed the National Forest area from 43,000,000 to 194,000,000 acres.

Five new national parks were begun. One was the Grand Canyon.

Fifty-one wild bird refuges and two national game preserves were set up. One was just for buffalo.

The wave of change that swept through Roosevelt's term of office continued. The new president, William Howard Taft, and Woodrow Wilson, who followed him, made many good changes.

On election night, the Wilsons waited for the voting results at their home in New Jersey. A message was handed to Mrs. Wilson.

Wilson had been a teacher as well as the president of Princeton University. Now the students formed a parade and came to celebrate.

I have no feeling of victory. I know that I have an important job to do.

She moved to Wilson's side.

My dear, I want to be the first to congratulate you. You are the second Democratic president since the Civil War.

He spoke to Congress on April 7, 1913.

We made the American people a promise...of a New Freedom. I call upon you to help this come true!

With Wilson leading, Congress acted.

This will lower the tariff rates. It's the first true tariff reform since the Civil War!

And added to the tariff act is an income tax. It was allowed by the sixteenth amendment to the Constitution.

Samuel Gompers, president of the AFL, liked a law that was passed in 1914.

The Federal Reserve Act changed the nation's banking system. But not everyone liked it.

The Federal Trade Commission and the Clayton Anti-trust Act are good. I thank you.

I say to you, this bill is not legal!

But it was passed. It was soon called the most important money law made since Alexander Hamilton's day.

In August, 1914, World War I broke out in Europe. Germany moved into Belgium to attack France. Austria - Hungary and Turkey joined Germany. England and Russia stood by France.

A war between great powers? Not in this modern age! We must stay out of it—or every change we have made will be lost.

On August 4, Wilson announced that America would not enter the war.

The United States must be neutral in fact as well as in name.

England decided to block ships going to Germany. Her navy stopped neutral ships and searched them for war goods. Whenever they were found, they were taken. This angered Americans, but no lives were lost and the goods taken were paid for. But Germany did more than this.

On February 4, 1915, the emperor of Germany made an announcement.

All waters around England are in a war zone. Any merchant ship found there will be destroyed!

On May 1, an American ship was torpedoed and sunk. On May 7, the British ship *Lusitania* was torpedoed off the Irish coast. It sank in fifteen minutes.

1,198 people died. 128 of them were Americans.

By law, if a warship takes or destroys a merchant ship, it must get the people to safety. But the German submarines strike without warning and kill all on board!

I will tell this to Germany in the strongest terms. But I will not be pushed into war! We are not ready. The people are divided in their feelings. I hate war!

Germany thought that America would not fight because she was weak. Becoming certain that America would not fight, Germany announced a submarine war. She sank many neutral ships, including American ships. Wilson spoke to Congress on April 2, 1917.

The night before, he walked the floors of the White House.

The next evening, he asked Congress to make war on Germany.

What else can I do? Is there anything else I can do?

It is a fearful thing to lead this great peaceful people into war. We shall fight for freedom, and for the rights and liberties of small nations.

No. Germany has forced the war upon the United States.

Across Europe, on the fields of the Western front, the fighting went on.

In the battle of Verdun, the French stopped a German advance—and lost 350,000 men.

In the battle of the Somme, a new weapon, the tank, was used. The French lost 200,000 men, the British 400,000. They won only a few miles of land.

After the United States entered the war, Congress at once passed a Selective Service Act.

All men between the ages of 21 and 31 years of age will wait for a call to military duty...

Our only other draft call, during the Civil War, caused riots. Will our people accept one today?

I think they will prove loyal, Mr. President.

On June 27 1918, Secretary of War Baker drew the first number for the draft.

To the joy and pride of America, the draft was carried out with ease. Soon 4,000,000 men were drafted. About half reached the fighting line.

After several months in training camps, the troops were loaded onto ships for the voyage to France.

They sailed in secret. No American ships were lost to submarines.

General John J. Pershing was given command of the U. S. Army. In 1918, he had bad news.

The Italian army has been smashed. And the Russians, after many German defeats, have left the war.

Leaving the Germans free to move many more soldiers to the French front?

Yes! In the spring the Germans will begin a great attack. Only fresh soldiers can save us. Will the Americans arrive in time?

It takes time to train soldiers. There are only 250,000 here now. I will push for one million by spring.

In March, the German leaders had a plan.

The Americans are getting ready for war. We must strike now before they come to help the French and English.

I will order an attack all along the line!

The German soldiers swept forward in a great attack.

The Germans took 3,000 square miles before they were stopped. But American soldiers were reaching Europe at the rate of 10,000 men a day.

Poor fellows! They've been fighting for four years.

They were rushed to the front to replace the tired English and French soldiers.

A great attack was planned in which 896,000 Americans took part.

The kaiser left his throne, and the Germans asked for peace. On November 11, 1918, President Wilson told the good news.

The armistice was signed this morning.

The Paris Peace Conference was held to draw up the treaty. The "Big Four" leaders of their countries were: Clemenceau of France, Lloyd George of Great Britain, Orlando of Italy, and President Wilson.

We must put away all weapons of war!

It is Germany who must put aside her weapons.

She must give up her colonies. The Rhineland should be taken away and given to France.

If Italy is not given Fiume, I will leave this conference.

Wilson refused to agree to some of the demands of England and France. While it was not as strong as these countries had wanted, the treaty was, of course, too harsh to suit Germany. What saved the group was the start of a League of Nations for settling future problems.

But in America a strange feeling was growing. Could it be that Wilson's own country would turn down the League? Senator Lodge spoke against it.

If we join, we in America must give up in part our freedom. We will have to subject our own will to the will of other nations.

He gave President Wilson an anti-League paper signed by thirty-seven senators.

Wilson spoke to his doctor, Dr. Grayson.

I must travel through the country. I must go to the people and tell them of the need for the League!

Mr. President, you can't do it! You're worn out! Your health won't stand it.

But Wilson went. For the next three weeks he travelled many miles, speaking two or three times a day.

In Pueblo, Colorado, he became very sick. He was hurried back to the White House.

He was never really well again.

On March 19, 1920, he was told that the Senate had voted 49 to 35 against the Treaty of Versailles.

I feel like going to bed and staying there.

In June, Wilson was visited by the Democratic candidate for president, James M. Cox, and the candidate for vice-president, Franklin D. Roosevelt.

Mr. President, we are a million percent with you...and that means the League of Nations!

Thank you very much.

But the Republican candidate, Warren Harding, was elected, and the United States did not join the League of Nations.

Wilson had spoken about the future.

If the United States does not join the League of Nations, there will be a breakup of the world. It will be much more than a war...

Dying in 1924, he did not live to see the start of World War II, less than twenty years later.

★★★

COMPLETE LIST OF POCKET CLASSICS AVAILABLE

CLASSICS

C 1 Black Beauty
C 2 The Call of the Wild
C 3 Dr. Jekyll and Mr. Hyde
C 4 Dracula
C 5 Frankenstein
C 6 Huckleberry Finn
C 7 Moby Dick
C 8 The Red Badge of Courage
C 9 The Time Machine
C10 Tom Sawyer
C11 Treasure Island
C12 20,000 Leagues Under the Sea
C13 The Great Adventures of Sherlock Holmes
C14 Gulliver's Travels
C15 The Hunchback of Notre Dame
C16 The Invisible Man
C17 Journey to the Center of the Earth
C18 Kidnapped
C19 The Mysterious Island
C20 The Scarlet Letter
C21 The Story of My Life
C22 A Tale of Two Cities
C23 The Three Musketeers
C24 The War of the Worlds
C25 Around the World in Eighty Days
C26 Captains Courageous
C27 A Connecticut Yankee in King Arthur's Court
C28 The Hound of the Baskervilles
C29 The House of the Seven Gables
C30 Jane Eyre
C31 The Last of the Mohicans
C32 The Best of O. Henry
C33 The Best of Poe
C34 Two Years Before the Mast
C35 White Fang
C36 Wuthering Heights
C37 Ben Hur
C38 A Christmas Carol
C39 The Food of the Gods
C40 Ivanhoe
C41 The Man in the Iron Mask
C42 The Prince and the Pauper
C43 The Prisoner of Zenda
C44 The Return of the Native
C45 Robinson Crusoe
C46 The Scarlet Pimpernel

COMPLETE LIST OF POCKET CLASSICS AVAILABLE
(cont'd)

SHAKESPEARE

HISTORY

COMPLETE LIST OF POCKET CLASSICS AVAILABLE
(cont'd)

BIOGRAPHIES

B 1 Charles Lindbergh
B 2 Amelia Earhart
B 3 Houdini
B 4 Walt Disney
B 5 Davy Crockett
B 6 Daniel Boone
B 7 Elvis Presley
B 8 The Beatles
B 9 Benjamin Franklin
B10 Martin Luther King, Jr.
B11 Abraham Lincoln
B12 Franklin D. Roosevelt
B13 George Washington
B14 Thomas Jefferson
B15 Madame Curie
B16 Albert Einstein
B17 Thomas Edison
B18 Alexander Graham Bell
B19 Vince Lombardi
B20 Pelé
B21 Babe Ruth
B22 Jackie Robinson
B23 Jim Thorpe
B24 Althea Gibson